Pierre the Peacock

Jocelyn M. Lacey

In loving memory
of my father, Dr. Jerry Mooneyhan,
whom the character Jerry
is named after.

In honor of my wonderful husband,
Steven Lacey, who has been so
supportive every step
of the way.

Pierre the Peacock

Written by Jocelyn M. Lacey
Illustrated by Teresa Wilkerson
Book Design by Tara Sizemore
Published October 2017
Little Creek Books
Imprint of Jan-Carol Publishing, Inc

Copyright © Jocelyn M. Lacey
ISBN: 978-1-945619-44-1
Library of Congress Control Number: 2017958208

You may contact the publisher:
Jan-Carol Publishing, Inc.
PO Box 701
Johnson City, TN 37605
publisher@jancarolpublishing.com
jancarolpublishing.com

Jan-Carol Publishing, Inc

"every story needs a book"

Letter to the Reader

It is my hope that you enjoy reading this story as much as I enjoyed writing it. May we all learn something, just as Pierre the Peacock did.

Acknowledgments

The idea of writing about a peacock came to me when a peacock showed up at my back door after I had just moved to a new state and was getting settled in the new house. I became interested in learning about everything that peacocks symbolize.

There once was a peacock named Pierre.
Pierre was a very handsome fellow.
He had a full tail with beautifully colored
feathers of the prettiest blues, greens,
browns, and yellows that you've ever seen.

There was only one problem, though.
Pierre knew how beautiful he was.
He constantly bragged about how attractive
he was. He was always quick to tell everyone
he saw how they were lucky to see such
a pretty creature like him.

Pierre did not realize it, but it was very annoying to everyone he came in contact with. He did not have any friends because they did not like the way he talked about himself and how pretty he thought he was. Pierre did not understand why he didn't have any friends. Who wouldn't want to be his friend and be seen with him since he was so pretty?
He thought that they were just jealous of him.

One day, Pierre met a little boy named Jerry.
Pierre said to him, "Hello, little boy.
Have you ever seen a creature so pretty?
Look at the colors in my tail. Aren't they a sight?"

The little boy said, "My name is Jerry.
The only colors I see on your tail are shades
of gray, black, and white."

Pierre couldn't believe it.
"What? You mean you can't see the blues,
greens, browns, and yellows in my beautiful tail?"

"No," replied Jerry. "I am colorblind."

"Colorblind?" Pierre asked. "What does that mean?"

Jerry responded, "Colorblind means that I can't
make out certain colors. What is blue to you
is gray for me. The only colors I can see
are shades of gray, black, and white."

Pierre couldn't believe it. "Since you can't see how beautiful my colors are, I guess you don't want to be my friend then, do you?"

Jerry replied, "I don't want to be your friend based on what you look like. I want to be your friend if you are nice and caring, someone I enjoy being around and can count on."

Pierre was surprised. "You mean it doesn't matter what I look like, as long as I am a good friend? I don't know how to be a friend. I've never had a friend before."

Jerry explained to Pierre, "It's probably because you are always telling everyone how pretty you think you are. No one wants to be around someone who brags about themselves."

"People notice the beauty of someone by the way they act. They will notice it on their own and not by having it pointed out to them. Your beauty will be seen when you show your true colors. You should treat others the way you would like to be treated."

This was all news to Pierre! He had no idea.
He was so glad that he had met Jerry.
No one had ever taken the time to tell this to him.

Jerry went on to say, "You need to embrace what you stand for. Peacocks are a wonderful example of standing tall and walking with their head held high, which makes everyone else want to do the same."

"What else do I stand for?" he asked Jerry.

"Well," Jerry replied, "Peacocks are also watchful and protective."

This made sense to Pierre, as he had just met Jerry and he was already protective of him. He was grateful that Jerry pointed out that beauty comes from within and that as long as he was nice to others, his beauty would shine and would enhance his beautiful colors on the outside, too.

With that, he and Jerry became very good friends and enjoyed spending time together. Pierre loved the friendship he had with Jerry and planned to be friends with him forever.

About the Author

Jocelyn Mooneyhan Lacey is a native of Johnson City, TN where she graduated from Science Hill High School and East Tennessee State University with a B.A. in Mass Communications. She met her husband, Steven Lacey, at ETSU and have since lived in Maine, Rhode Island, the Outer Banks of North Carolina, and they have since settled in New Jersey for the time being. She also shares her home with two dogs, a cat, and three fish. While she has written other children's stories, this is the first one to be published. You can contact the author via e-mail at Hapigirl10@hotmail.com or on Instagram with the username Hapigirl10.

CPSIA information can be obtained
at www.ICGtesting.com
Printed in the USA
BVHW021930140820
586439BV00006B/373